Appleby, William
   The sleeping Beauty
and The Firebird

THE SLEEPING BEAUTY
and
THE FIREBIRD

THE YOUNG READER'S GUIDES TO MUSIC

THE SLEEPING BEAUTY

and

THE FIREBIRD

Stories from the Ballet

BY

WILLIAM APPLEBY

and

FREDERICK FOWLER

Illustrated by

ALAN CLARK

NEW YORK

HENRY Z. WALCK, INCORPORATED

1965

Library of Congress Catalog
Card Number: 65–13226

Printed in Great Britain by
Richard Clay (The Chaucer Press) Ltd.,
Bungay, Suffolk

CONTENTS

THE SLEEPING BEAUTY

THE FIREBIRD

The Sleeping Beauty

CHAPTER I

AURORA'S CHRISTENING

THE four trumpeters raised their golden instruments to their lips and played a fanfare which echoed through the lofty royal ballroom. The gilded doors were opened by huge burly guards and two more guests entered the room.

Waiting to greet them was the Lord High Chamberlain, Cantalbutte, in his ceremonial dress of black and gold. In a loud voice he announced their names; then the newcomers joined the lords and ladies already assembled. The doors closed again as Cantalbutte put on his spectacles, peered at his scroll on which the names of all the guests were written, and added two more ticks. Again the trumpets sounded and the doors opened. Again Cantalbutte's voice was heard as more guests arrived and had their names ticked off. Soon the room was full of noble lords and ladies who had been summoned by the King to witness the christening of his infant daughter, Princess Aurora.

From the ceiling hundreds of lights, in their crystal chandeliers, twinkled down on the scarlet and gold uniforms of the men and the bejewelled silks and velvets of their ladies. Flowers of all scents and sizes entwined the marble columns. The golden cradle of the infant princess, with the ever-watchful royal nurse-maids, stood on a platform at one end of the room. Through the noise of trumpets, the announcements of Cantalbutte and the gossip of the guests, the Princess Aurora slept peacefully. At the other end of the room, on a higher platform and under crimson canopies, stood the empty thrones waiting for the King and Queen.

Suddenly the trumpets were heard again. This time they played louder and longer than before. The lords and ladies ceased their chatter and looked towards the doors. Putting his spectacles away, Cantalbutte stood to attention. The doors opened and King Florestan XXIV entered with his Queen, followed by a long train of attendants. The guests bowed as the Royal procession made its way slowly towards the cradle.

'How beautiful she is!' said the Queen, looking down on her golden-haired Aurora.

'A very good-natured and contented child!' replied the King. He took the Queen's arm and led her towards the thrones at the other end of the ballroom.

It was then the turn of the guests to file past and look into the cradle.

'She's just like an angel,' said one.

'Hair like pure gold,' remarked another.

'Look! she smiles in her sleep,' a third whispered, while a fourth was heard to say, 'How like her mother she is.'

Princess Aurora slept on and neither saw nor heard the guests as they passed by. When they had all seen the Princess, Cantalbutte's voice was heard again, announcing the arrival of the six fairy-godmothers. A fanfare greeted each fairy as she appeared. First came the Fairy of the Crystal Fountain, in a dress of sparkling whites and blues. She curtsied before the King and Queen, and then danced down the room towards the royal cradle. Near it she placed her gift, a crown of water-lilies. Wearing a floral dress, the Fairy of the Magic Garden came next, dancing her way to the cradle, gazing down on the sleeping infant, and putting her gift near the water-lily crown.

'The Fairy of the Woodland Glades!' shouted Cantalbutte as the next one entered, and she was soon followed by the Fairy of the Song Birds. The fifth Fairy, the Fairy of the Golden Vine, was in a dazzling dress of gold. She placed her gift alongside the others, the water-lily crown, the basket of flowers, the wild fruits of the woodlands, and the song-bird in the cage. The final fanfare rang out and everyone knew, from the colour of her

The Lilac Fairy

dress that it was the Lilac Fairy. After her curtsey she raised her wand as she smiled on the child. She was just going to place her gift with the others when a vivid flash of lightning made everyone jump. Before they recovered from their surprise, a terrific crack of thunder rocked the room. Princess Aurora awoke and cried.

CHAPTER II

THE CURSE OF CARABOSSE

EFORE the sound of thunder had died away the ballroom doors burst open and a breathless messenger hurried towards Cantalbutte.

'Oh, sire,' he gasped as he fell on his knees before the Lord High Chamberlain, 'The Fairy Carabosse is approaching in her carriage.'

'The Fairy Carabosse,' echoed Cantalbutte, turning pale.

'Yes, sire,' continued the messenger. 'She is in a violent temper because you did not invite her to the christening. She is making the earth tremble with her thunder and splitting the skies with her lightning.'

'What is it, what is it?' shouted King Florestan from his throne. Cantalbutte, trembling all over, turned towards the King and Queen.

'Your Majesties,' he stammered, 'the Fairy Carabosse caused the lightning to flash and the thunder to peal. She is coming here now in a great temper.'

'Why, what has upset her?' the Queen asked.

'Oh, pardon me, your Majesties, but I forgot to invite her to the christening,' answered poor Cantalbutte, sinking still farther to the floor.

'You forgot!' roared the King, seizing the scroll from his

Lord High Chamberlain and looking quickly at the names of all the guests. 'You stupid nincompoop!' he screamed, throwing the scroll at Cantalbutte. His face became redder and redder, while the Queen went whiter and whiter. The poor Lord High Chamberlain shook in every limb and his teeth chattered in his nodding head.

With a sudden roar the doors flew open again. In rushed a coach pulled by four giant rats. Vultures flew overhead. As the coach jerked to a halt before the royal thrones a figure with gleaming green eyes, pointed nose, and long finger-nails alighted and strode up to the King. It was the wicked Fairy Carabosse. She was dressed in black from head to foot and carried a crooked stick in one hand.

'I demand an explanation!' she snarled. 'Why wasn't I invited to the christening?'

'It was all my fault,' said the unfortunate Cantalbutte. 'I assure you I did not mean to forget you. Please accept my humble apology.'

'Your fault,' said the fairy, turning to Cantalbutte. 'Take that! and that!' and she pulled him round the room by his hair and hit him with her stick.

'Mercy!' wailed the wretched Lord High Chamberlain, who was bruised all over and was losing great tufts of hair.

The Queen stepped down from her throne and pleaded with the angry fairy. 'Oh, Carabosse,' she said, 'do not spoil the christening. Please forgive us for forgetting to invite you, and be our guest for the day.'

'I'm not staying where I am not wanted,' replied Carabosse. 'I'm going, but before I go——'

'Mercy!' wailed the Lord High Chamberlain

* 7 *

'Yes?' said the Queen.

There was an evil glint in the fairy's eyes and a wicked grin on her face as she continued: 'Before I go I must not forget my gift to your infant child.' She looked round the room at all the anxious faces. 'My gift is a curse!' she screamed. There was a gasp of horror from the guests. 'The child will grow up to be beautiful. She will be strong and healthy, good and clever, but——' The wicked fairy paused and there was a deathly silence in the room. 'Before she is eighteen years old she will prick her finger and die.'

King Florestan's crown clattered to the floor. The sobbing Queen collapsed on her throne. With an unearthly cackle Carabosse jumped into her coach, cracked her whip and drove from the room. Outside, the lightning tore the skies and thunder rolled round the heavens. Inside, there was sadness and confusion. The King tried to console his heartbroken Queen. Cantalbutte wished he was dead. The tears of the nursemaids fell into the royal cradle. Suddenly the voice of the Lilac Fairy was heard.

'Pray do not grieve, your Majesties,' she said, 'for I have not yet made my gift to my god-child.'

Everyone turned to listen to the fairy in the lilac dress. The ladies dried their tears and even Cantalbutte looked more hopeful.

'My gift to the Princess Aurora,' the Lilac Fairy continued, 'is life, not death. One day she will prick her finger as the evil Fairy Carabosse said, but she will not die. She will fall into a long, deep sleep. She will sleep until a prince awakens her with a kiss.'

On hearing this good news the Lord High Chamberlain jumped in the air and danced a jig around the room. Full of joy, the King and Queen with the fairy-godmothers and all the guests gathered round the royal cradle. Princess Aurora was sleeping peacefully again.

CHAPTER III

AURORA'S BIRTHDAY

GRADUALLY the years passed by. King Florestan became a little fatter, the Queen's hair began to show touches of silver, and the Lord High Chamberlain got balder and balder. Princess Aurora, however, grew more beautiful each year, and everything possible was done to prevent her from pricking herself. Neither pins nor needles were allowed in the palace. Wherever the Princess went the royal nurse went too, always guarding her closely. They shielded her from prickly plants and long-clawed cats. All visitors to the palace were searched to see that they brought nothing with them that was sharp or pointed.

On Aurora's sixteenth birthday the palace grounds were crowded with people, for everyone in the country had been invited to her party. Lords and Ladies mingled with villagers in admiring the flowers, the fountains, and the strutting peacocks. Children chased each other over the lawns and counted the darting goldfish in the ponds. A great cheer rang out when the King and Queen with their attendants came down the path from the palace to the thrones set up by the edge of a large lawn on which the festivities were to take place. With them were four princes, an Indian prince, an Italian, a Polish, and an English prince, each of whom wished to marry Aurora. Hundreds of guests lined the edges of the lawn to watch the performance. First came a dance by village maidens who moved gracefully over the grass, each holding above her head a large hoop garlanded with flowers. Next it was Aurora's turn to entertain. There were gasps of admiration when the tall and graceful Princess, smiling with happiness, stepped forward to begin her dance. Her long silk dress, pale pink in colour, was studded with diamonds which flashed with her every movement. 'Encore!' the excited crowd shouted as her dance ended, and so the delighted Princess danced for them again. Afterwards, the four foreign princes were introduced to Aurora. Each of them danced with her in turn and presented her with a rose. This also pleased the on-lookers and so the four princes and Aurora came back and danced together.

Later, Aurora mingled with her guests around the lawn and watched the rest of the entertainment. She was enjoying a dance by the maids of honour when suddenly she felt someone touch her arm. On looking round she saw an old woman dressed from head to foot in black. Her back was bent, she was leaning on a crooked stick and her face was hidden behind a long black scarf. In one hand she held a strange object.

'This is a birthday gift for you, my dear,' she said, holding out a strange looking piece of wood to the Princess. Aurora was fascinated by this gift, for she had never seen anything like it before. She did not know that it was a spindle used in the spin-ning of wool from sheep. Almost every house in the country had its spinning wheel and spindle, but none could be found in the palace, for spindles were sharp and pointed, and spindles could prick.

'Thank you very much indeed,' said the Princess, but when she looked up the strange figure in black had disappeared. Aurora ran across the grass towards the royal thrones, carrying the spindle in one hand.

The birthday present

'What is that you have?' said the Queen anxiously, 'give it to me at once.'

'Oh, no mother, please, I want to keep it,' replied the Princess hiding it behind her back.

'Drop it this moment!' cried the Queen, rising to her feet. Full of mischief Aurora shook her head and danced away across the lawn, throwing the spindle from one hand to the other.

Poor Cantalbutte was again trembling from head to foot, for he knew that he would be blamed for the presence of the mysterious old woman in black. He had stood for hours by the gate making sure that nobody brought any scratchy object with them. He

She fell at their feet

had turned away four village women who were bringing their knitting and their knitting needles. Now he was watching the princess dance around holding a sharp spindle. It was all most distressing.

Suddenly Aurora stopped. She felt a twinge of pain shoot up her arm. She had pricked herself. Throwing away the spindle and sucking her blood-stained finger she hurried back towards her mother.

* 13 *

'Aurora! Aurora! What has happened?' said King Florestan anxiously as he hurried towards her with the Queen.

'Oh, it's nothing,' replied Aurora bravely, but she already had a strange feeling in her legs, and all the people seemed to her to be spinning round and round. She felt the grass coming up to meet her. She thought she saw an old woman in black laughing at her. She struggled on towards her mother and father and fell in a heap at their feet.

CHAPTER IV

THE ENCHANTMENT

THE birthday party which had begun so happily was now a scene of sadness and confusion. Hundreds of guests crowded round the spot where the Princess had fallen.

'Stand back, stand back, please!' urged the Lord High Chamberlain, but he pleaded in vain, for everyone wished to see what was happening. The Queen gently placed her arms around her daughter's shoulders and tried to raise her from the ground.

'Aurora!' she whispered, 'please speak to me, oh! speak to me.' But the Princess's body hung limply, as if she were dead. Her face was deathly white and the silvery pink dress was stained with blood from her finger. King Florestan, looking up from his daughter for a minute, saw a figure in black watching from behind a distant tree. The black scarf had fallen away from her, and he could recognize the evil face of the Fairy Carabosse.

'Seize that woman!' he commanded, and instantly the four foreign princes drew their swords and dashed after the wicked fairy who disappeared into the woods. At that moment the Lilac Fairy appeared as if from nowhere.

'Do not despair, your Majesties,' she said. 'Your daughter is not dead, she only sleeps. Carry her to her room and put her to bed.'

Before this could be done the sound of approaching footsteps made everyone turn. The four princes were coming back from the woods and it was plain to see that they had been unsuccessful. The Prince of England spoke for all of them.

The Sleeping Beauty

'I am sorry, your Majesty,' he said, bowing low, 'but the evil creature has escaped. We chased her here and there through the trees. Gradually we were getting nearer to her. She was almost within our grasp when there was a blinding flash and a cloud of smoke. When the smoke cleared she had vanished.'

* 16 *

'Thank you, all of you,' the King replied quietly. 'And now pray, carry my daughter into the palace.'

The four princes carefully lifted the sleeping girl and headed the procession along the winding paths, up the marble steps and

The palace is enchanted

through the wide doors into the palace. Across the great hall they went and up the red-carpeted staircase to Aurora's bedroom. They gently laid the princess on the bed and drew the bedclothes over her. Everyone stood back a little, leaving the King and Queen at the bedside looking down on their daughter. Even in deep sleep she was still beautiful, with her long, golden hair covering the pillows.

The Lilac Fairy raised her wand. Immediately everyone in the palace went to sleep just where they were. With closed eyes the King and Queen stood asleep at the bedside. The four foreign princes stood like statues. Nearby was Cantalbutte, perfectly still and no longer trembling. By the doors the burly guards were motionless, like huge figures carved in stone. Below in the courtyard the royal hounds, no longer watchful, squatted with closed eyes outside their kennels. The cook slept in her rocking chair, still holding a basin in one hand and clutching a spoon in the other. Only the Lilac Fairy was awake. Once more she raised her wand. In a twinkling, tall trees shot up through the lawns and flower-beds and completely surrounded the palace. Ivy and other creeping plants quickly climbed the walls and smothered the windows. Doorways disappeared behind a tangled growth of tall grasses. Thorny brambles crept and crawled like snakes over all the paths.

No longer could the palace be seen. No longer could the palace be reached and entered. The Lilac Fairy looked down on her work, smiled, and disappeared.

CHAPTER V

PRINCE CHARMING MEETS THE LILAC FAIRY

ONE hundred years passed and people forgot all about the sleeping Princess. The palace, completely buried by tall trees and tangled undergrowth, was also forgotten.

Our story now takes us to a far-off country, in which dwelt a young prince. His real name was Florimund, but, because of his handsome appearance most people called him Prince Charming. One morning he set off from his castle, accompanied by many noble lords and ladies, to hunt the wild boar. All day they searched without success for signs of these savage creatures, and, as evening came, they found themselves in a forest clearing by the side of a stream. There they sat down to eat and rest while the servants opened the baskets of food and wine.

'Come on!' said one of the ladies, after they had finished the meal, 'let us have games and dances. This clearing is just the place for them.'

Quickly a target was set up and shooting practice began. Arrows whizzed through the air and a great cheer rang out whenever someone scored a bull's-eye. When they tired of shooting they played other games and when they tired of games they turned to dancing. Everyone was happy except the Prince. He joined in neither the games nor the dancing, but sat some distance away on a fallen tree-trunk, with his head in his hands. He was tired of life at the castle, with its endless round of games and dancing, of feasting and hunting. How he wished that he could go on a real adventure. He imagined himself riding off with shield and spear to kill a dangerous dragon, or saving a beautiful maiden from the clutches of an evil witch. He was tired of having nothing to do but enjoy himself.

Suddenly, a wild boar was sighted some distance away. The dancing stopped, spears were seized, and everybody dashed off in pursuit. Only the Prince remained, still sitting there as darkness came and the moon cast its reflection on the water. For a while everything was silent. Then the Prince heard a movement from the stream. He looked towards it and saw a boat coming in his direction. It was not an ordinary boat, for its sides were made of mother-of-pearl, and from its prow silken threads rose into the air where they were harnessed to giant butterflies which pulled the vessel along. Slowly it glided to the water's edge and someone stepped out. It was the Lilac Fairy.

'Good day, Prince Charming,' she greeted him, 'why do you sit alone in the forest at nightfall? Where are your companions?'

'Oh, they are hunting the wild boar,' he replied. 'They are always hunting wild boar, or playing games like small children, or making themselves dizzy with dancing.'

'Well, what would you rather do?' the Fairy asked.

'Something quite different,' answered the Prince, 'something exciting and worth-while, something I have never done before.'

The Lilac Fairy was silent for a while. Then she said, 'How would you like to go to a distant land and find the Sleeping Beauty?'

'The Sleeping Beauty?' said the astonished Prince. 'I have never heard of her. Who is she?'

Sitting down beside him the Lilac Fairy told the story of the lovely Aurora, the evil Carabosse, and the forgotten palace.

Prince Charming meets the Lilac Fairy

'A pretty tale,' said the Prince, when she had finished, 'but it is not true, is it?'

'Quite true,' replied the Lilac Fairy. 'Look, I will show you the Sleeping Beauty.'

She waved her wand and in the clouds appeared a picture of

Aurora in her bed surrounded by all the sleeping figures. She raised her wand again, the picture vanished and another came. Aurora was dancing on the grass at her sixteenth birthday party.

'How beautiful she is,' sighed the Prince. 'Please tell me how I can find her.'

'Come along,' said the Lilac Fairy. 'I will take you.'

Together they boarded the boat which glided away downstream. No sound was heard save for the lapping of the waves and the beating wings of the butterflies. They sailed for hundreds of miles through many countries. They sailed through autumn, where brown and gold leaves dropped on the water. They sailed through winter, with its ice and snow. Soon it was spring. The birds sang and the trees were covered with blossom. The sun shone more strongly still and they sailed into summer.

'We are nearly there,' said the Lilac Fairy.

CHAPTER VI

THE SPELL IS BROKEN

SLOWLY the boat came to rest at the stream's edge and Prince Charming helped the Lilac Fairy to alight. Before them stood a dense wood. The Lilac Fairy seemed to know the Prince's thoughts, for she suddenly said:

'Yes, this is the wood which hides the palace. We are its first visitors for one hundred years.'

The Prince stood looking at the tall trees rising everywhere

Before them stood a dense wood

from the tangled mass of creeping plants. He glanced up at the
spreading branches which shut out the daylight, then turning to
the Fairy he said:

'Surely we need an army of woodcutters to hack a path
through this wood to the palace!'

The secret path

'Oh, no!' she replied, 'there is a path known only to me.
Follow and I will show you.' She led him round the edge of the
wood until they came to a weeping-willow tree. Parting its
drooping branches with her wand, she beckoned the Prince to
enter. They found themselves in a low tunnel, with branches
just above their heads and the trunks of trees rising on either
side. Carefully they made their way over gnarled roots and

crackling twigs in almost complete darkness. Startled rabbits scurried away as they approached. Blind-flying bats brushed against their faces. The path twisted this way and that as it went, but the Lilac Fairy knew the way and the Prince followed close behind her. He was wondering how much farther they had to go when the fairy stopped and pointed towards the ground. In the gloom, the Prince could just see a flight of stone steps leading upwards. A carpet of moss covered each step and pointed ferns peeped through the cracks in the stonework. The two figures climbed slowly upwards until they found themselves in the courtyard of the palace. They stepped over the sleeping hounds and reached an ivy-covered door. Startled birds flew from their shelter as the Lilac Fairy and Prince Charming tore down long streamers of ivy, opened the door, and walked along a corridor curtained with cobwebs. They passed the kitchens where the cook still slept in her rocking-chair, with tarnished spoon in one hand, the dust-filled bowl in the other. They came to the great hall, now damp and gloomy, for no light passed through its tree-covered windows. Up the main staircase they felt their way, past silent footmen and sleeping maidservants, until they reached the door of Aurora's bedroom. The tall guards were no longer guarding. Motionless they stood as the Prince and the Lilac Fairy passed them and entered the bedroom.

The Prince could not help giving a gasp of surprise at the sight before him. There on the bed was the sleeping princess. On one side stood King Florestan and his Queen, with the Lord High Chamberlain, Cantalbutte, behind them. On the other side stood the foreign princes with their attendants.

'Have these people been standing up asleep for a hundred years?' the startled Prince exclaimed.

'For one hundred years exactly,' replied the Lilac Fairy.

The Prince moved on tiptoe to the edge of the bed as if he was afraid that a noise would awaken the sleepers. He looked on the face of Aurora with her golden hair still gleaming on the pillow.

'How beautiful she is,' he whispered as he leaned over and kissed her cold lips. He moved away quickly, held his breath, and waited to see what would happen. Slowly the Princess turned on to her back, opened her eyes and smiled at the Prince. At the same time there were other movements in the room. The King and Queen came towards the bed as if they had never been asleep at all, and old Cantalbutte trotted behind them. The four foreign princes opened their eyes and continued a conversation they had been having one hundred years earlier. The room suddenly became bright when the Lilac Fairy waved her wand and the wood outside disappeared. Sunlight streamed in and the dust and cobwebs vanished. Outside, the lawns and flower beds, the lakes and the fountains could be seen again, just as they had been a century before, on Aurora's sixteenth birthday. The silence of the palace was broken, and everywhere there was happy and excited chatter.

'Oh, my Aurora!' sighed the Queen, as she held her daughter close to her. Tears of joy were running down her face.

'How can I thank you?' said the King, as he grasped the Prince's hand. Before the Prince could reply, King Florestan continued: 'Oh—I know, I suppose you wish to marry my daughter?'

'If your Majesty pleases,' murmured the Prince, bowing low.

'Certainly, my boy, certainly!' And the excited King gave the Prince a hearty pat on his back and dashed off to join the Queen. The Lord High Chamberlain, who had overheard the conversation rubbed his hands with delight, for there was nothing he liked better than organizing christenings, birthdays, and weddings. Prince Charming, left on his own, went over to join Aurora.

'Come along,' she said to him, 'let me show you our beautiful gardens.' He took her hand and together they made their way out into the sunshine.

CHAPTER VII

AURORA'S WEDDING

THE royal ballroom in King Florestan's palace was once more filled with guests. This time they had come, not to a christening, nor to a birthday party, but to the wedding of Prince Charming and Princess Aurora. From the ceiling the hundreds of lights, in their crystal chandeliers, again twinkled down on scarlet and gold uniforms and bejewelled silks and velvets. The King and Queen sat enthroned under the crimson canopies. The Lord High Chamberlain, Cantalbutte, determined that nothing should go wrong this time, rushed hither and thither seeing that all orders were being obeyed. Then, like a faithful sheepdog, he returned to his place at the King's side.

Suddenly, the four trumpeters raised their golden instruments and played a fanfare. The doors opened, and the bride and bridegroom entered, followed by their bridesmaids and pages and also by the six fairy-godmothers. How lovely Aurora looked as she walked arm in arm with her beloved husband, smiling and acknowledging the bowing and curtsying of her guests.

Again the trumpets rang out and again the doors opened. There was a murmur of excitement in the room as a strange procession entered. The people of storyland were coming to offer their gifts and to dance at the wedding.

'Look!' said one of the guests, 'there's Puss in Boots with the white cat.'

'Yes, and do you see who's coming in now? It's little Red Riding Hood with the wolf close behind her.'

The giant and Hop o' my Thumb

'Why, there's Cinderella and her Prince!' another guest exclaimed, 'but I don't know the golden-haired girl talking to them.'

'Don't you?' someone answered. 'Why, that's Goldilocks.' There was a gasp of surprise as a huge giant entered, stooping as he did so, in order to get through the door. Clinging tightly to his shoulder was Hop o' my Thumb, and not far behind came Beauty and the Beast. The guests moved back towards the walls, leaving a space in the centre of the ballroom, where these well-beloved characters from Fairy Tale and Nursery Rhyme could dance in honour of the bride and bridegroom.

Everyone enjoyed the dance of Puss-in-Boots and the White Cat, and there was great excitement when poor little Red Riding Hood, with her basket of food was chased and caught

Off on their honeymoon

by the wicked wolf. Everyone laughed at the antics of the tiny Hop o' my Thumb and the giant, and admired the graceful movements of Cinderella and her Prince. There was much clapping and cheering when the performance ended, and the cheering broke out again when it became known that Prince Charming and Aurora were going to dance also.

So the happy party went on, with neither thunder and lightning nor wicked fairies to spoil it. The Fairy Carabosse was forgotten. She had not been seen for many years, and some said that she had been killed by one of her own flashes of lightning. Before the party ended the King and Queen, Prince Charming and Princess Aurora, and all the guests joined in the dancing, and the room was filled with graceful movement.

Soon it was time for the Prince and Princess to depart for their honeymoon. The guests followed them from the palace, down the paths and past the flower beds to the banks of the stream. Raising her wand, the Lilac Fairy blessed the happy pair. The mother-of-pearl boat glided to the bank and the Prince and Princess entered. The wings of the butterflies began to beat, slowly at first and then faster. The boat moved away amid cries of 'Good-bye' and the waving of hands. The King and Queen stood there with their guests until they could no longer see their daughter and the boat was a mere speck in the distance.

CHAPTER VIII

THE MUSIC

ABOUT three hundred years ago a Frenchman named Charles Perrault was writing fairy tales. Perrault was born in the year 1628, and before his death in 1703 his story-writing had made him famous. Although you may never have heard of him by name, you are sure to know some of his stories. They include 'Little Red Riding Hood', 'Puss in Boots', 'Cinderella', 'Tom Thumb', and 'The Sleeping Beauty'. He wrote them in French, of course, and the French title for 'The Sleeping Beauty' is '*La Belle au Bois Dormant*', which really means 'The Beauty in the Sleeping Wood'.

Today these fairy tales are known all over the world. Small children love to listen as they are told to them. Later they read them for themselves. When they are still older they meet them once again at the theatre, for many of Perrault's tales have been used in pantomime and ballet.

You may perhaps have been to a pantomime at Christmas. Quite often a pantomime has a fairy-tale title such as *Cinderella*, but the entertainment includes much more than the well-known story. In between scenes from the fairy tales there are the singers of comic songs, the clowns, the acrobats, the jugglers, and the dancers, all of whom have really nothing whatever to do with the fairy tale. Today a pantomime is more like a variety show and not at all like ballet, which tells the story through movement and dancing to the music of an orchestra, without using any words at all. Strangely enough, pantomime used to be quite like ballet a long time ago, for the word 'pantomime' means the telling of a story by miming, that is, without speech.

The story of the Sleeping Beauty that you have just read is the first half of Perrault's tale, which has been used for many years both in pantomime and ballet. At one time the title of the ballet was changed to *The Sleeping Princess* so that people would not mistake it for the pantomime. Today, however, the ballet is once more called *The Sleeping Beauty*.

The music for *The Sleeping Beauty* was written by Tchaikovsky. This famous Russian composer had already written the music for another well-known ballet, *Swan Lake*. In the year 1890, in the Russian capital of St. Petersburg, now Leningrad, *The Sleeping Beauty* was performed for the first time. Not long afterwards, Tchaikovsky started to write the music for the ballet *Nutcracker*. Today these three ballets with music by Tchaikovsky—*Swan Lake*, *The Sleeping Beauty*, and *Nutcracker*—are regularly performed in towns and cities throughout the world. You may be fortunate enough to see a performance. If not, you can still enjoy the music when it is performed on the radio or television, or can listen to some of it on phonograph records. Perhaps you play an instrument yourself. If so, try these tunes from The Sleeping Beauty on the piano, violin, recorder, or whatever instrument you play.

THE MUSIC

1. There are many famous waltzes in Tchaikovsky's ballet music. Do you remember the 'Waltz of the Flowers' in the *Nutcracker* ballet? Here is part of the well-known waltz from Act One of *The Sleeping Beauty*. It is the dance of the village maidens at Aurora's sixteenth birthday party.

2. This melody also comes in Act One during Aurora's sixteenth birthday party. It is known as the 'Rose Adagio'. You will remember that in the story the four foreign princes dance with Aurora and each presents her with a rose.

3. This is the Lilac Fairy's tune and occurs several times. It is heard when the Lilac Fairy orders that the sleeping Princess should be carried into the palace. It is heard again when the

Lilac Fairy, in the mother-of-pearl boat, meets Prince Charming as he sits alone in the forest clearing.

4. This melody is heard when Prince Charming steps into the Lilac Fairy's boat to go with her to discover the sleeping Princess.

5. This is heard in Act Three at the wedding celebrations when the people from fairyland give their performance. It is the beginning of the dance of Little Red Riding Hood and the Wolf. If you see a performance or hear a recording, listen for this tune on the woodwind, followed later by the growling of the wolf (strings).

6. This is also taken from the wedding celebrations in Act Three. The fairy-tale characters have finished their performance, and this is the beginning of Aurora's dance.

The Firebird

CHAPTER I

PRINCE IVAN GOES HUNTING

THROUGHOUT the day the sun had shone down on the village from a cloudless sky. It was the hottest day of the summer. Huge cracks were appearing in the parched earth, and the river, which had roared under the bridge all winter, was now a mere trickle. The green carpet of the fields had faded to one of yellows and browns. The small cottages were almost as hot as ovens, and everywhere people could be seen squatting out of doors in the shadows of their houses. Children sat outside too, wondering how to pass the time, for it was too hot to run and play. Mothers sang quietly as they nursed their fretful babies. Dogs crouched panting, their long tongues lolling from open jaws.

It was just as hot in the palace on the hill. It made the King angry, and he was forever shouting to his perspiring attendants, urging them to fan him more vigorously. The water in the marble ponds of the palace gardens was no longer cool, and the goldfish hid themselves under the huge floating lily-leaves. Beneath the palm trees in the courtyard Prince Ivan sat and talked to his friends for it was too hot to go hunting. Everyone, from the King down to the poorest peasant, rested and waited for the golden red ball of the sun to sink behind the western mountains.

With the evening came a refreshing breeze, and the village sprang to life. People began their neglected work, children played games, and the dogs sniffed about for food. The tired babies closed their eyes and fell asleep. The Prince Ivan decided to go for a long walk. Picking up his bow and arrows he opened the small gate in the palace wall and strode off in the direction of the forest. Soon he was walking silently and with a spring in each step on the carpet of leaf mould and pine needles in the gloom of the tall trees. From time to time he took quick aim at ghostly-looking owls and blind-flying bats, but in the dusk he missed his mark and lost his arrows.

After following the winding paths for several miles Ivan

decided to retrace his steps. Before long, however, he realized that he was lost, for night had fallen and the paths were no longer to be seen. He crashed helplessly through the under-growth and stumbled over the roots of trees. Suddenly he saw

Lost in the forest

something tall and greyish-white in front of him. He cautiously approached it and found it was a high wall that he had never seen before in all his forest wanderings. It was useless to try to climb it in the darkness, so he sat down with his back against it, deciding to rest there until daybreak. All was still and silent and dark, and very soon the Prince was fast asleep.

CHAPTER II

THE FIREBIRD

IVAN awoke with a start. He wondered what had disturbed him, for it was still night, and he could neither see nor hear anything in the darkness around him. He stared into the gloom and listened, but he was still very sleepy and before long his eyes were closing and his head nodding. Suddenly he was wide awake again as a bright light lit up the near-by trees and cast long dark shadows on the ground. This light, which danced about and made the shadows dance with it, seemed to be coming from over the high wall against which the Prince had been resting.

His eyes were closing and his head nodding

After a few minutes it vanished as quickly as it had come, and night returned to the forest.

'Most mysterious,' said Ivan to himself. 'If this strange light comes again I must find out what it is.'

He had not long to wait before it reappeared. Quickly his fingers and toes searched for cracks in the wall as he pulled himself up. When he reached the top and looked over, his eyes opened wide with amazement. Below him was a long green lawn surrounded by flowering shrubs and apple trees. The trees were laden with fruit, not ordinary fruit, but golden fruit which glittered in the light. Gliding in and out of the trees was a magnificent bird. Its long yellow and red feathers glowed like fire. Its eyes flashed like diamonds. Its wings were like flames. The curious light which had awakened the Prince was coming from this brilliant bird, and went with it as it flew backwards and forwards. Ivan's hands moved unthinkingly to his cross-bow, but he quickly drew them away.

'No, no!' he murmured to himself, 'I must not kill it. I will try to catch it and take it back with me to the palace. I have never seen a bird so beautiful. It is no ordinary bird, it is a bird of fire.'

Silently he climbed down into the garden and crept between the bushes towards the Firebird which was pecking at the golden apples on one of the trees. Nearer and nearer he crawled, and still the bird did not see him as it fluttered from one fruit to another. Ivan made a sudden dart forward and the bird was struggling in his hands. In vain it tried to escape. Its dazzling wings beat against his face and its shining beak pecked at his hands, but he refused to let it go. At last, tired with struggling,

The Firebird escapes

the Firebird sank exhausted in the Prince's arms. He almost dropped it with surprise when he heard it speaking to him.

'Let me go, please let me go,' it whimpered. Ivan found himself speaking back to it.

'No, no!' he said, 'I will not harm you, but I am taking you with me back to the palace.' The bird, in a last effort to save itself, turned its head and plucked a long orange-coloured feather from one of its wings.

'Take this,' it said, offering the feather to the Prince. 'Whenever you are in danger, wave this feather and I will come to your aid.' As Ivan lifted one hand and took the feather, the Firebird slipped from his grasp and flew away over the trees. Away it flew, getting smaller and smaller, until it finally disappeared and all was dark again.

CHAPTER III

A BALL GAME

IVAN sat under one of the trees laden with golden apples and waited for the night to end. Never before in all his visits to the forest had he seen this garden. At the palace of his father, the King, he had never heard anyone mention such a place and so he was determined to explore its every corner in the light of day before setting out on his homeward journey. He was too excited to sleep any more so he sat with his back against the tree-trunk and waited for the dawn. He had not long to wait, for daybreak comes early in the summer time. Soon the sky changed from black to grey and forest birds greeted the morning with their songs. Before long the clouds were tinged with gold when the first rays of the sun appeared. Ivan could now see clearly everything around him. He got up, rubbed his eyes and yawned as he stretched himself.

He found that the high wall over which he had climbed completely enclosed the garden, but in one of its sides there was a huge door set in a stone archway. He ran quickly to it, curious to find out what lay beyond, but it was bolted and barred on the other side. He pushed against it and tried to shake it but it would not yield. Its stout oak panels were as strong as the wall itself. 'If I cannot go through the wall I must climb over

D

* 43 *

it,' he said to himself. Just then he heard a noise on the other side so he darted behind a bush and waited.

Slowly the huge door creaked open and a group of barefooted maidens, in long white dresses, came running through on to the lawn. Ivan counted them. 'One, two, three . . . twelve altogether.' He had no sooner finished than another maiden appeared. She was the most beautiful girl he had ever seen. Her

Another maiden appeared

long golden hair floated behind her as she ran to join the others. 'She must be their leader,' thought Ivan, 'or perhaps she is a princess,' for although she was dressed in white like the others, her long gown was richly embroidered with thread of gold. The girls danced over the grass and up to the apple trees. They shook the branches and a shower of golden fruit fell to the ground. With shouts of joy they darted here and there picking them up. Ivan, from his leafy hiding place watched and wondered. 'Surely they cannot eat such fruit,' he thought, 'why do they gather it?'

He soon discovered the answer, for games began and the shining apples took the place of rubber balls. They flew through the air into hands outstretched to catch them. Back again they were hurled, gleaming and glittering as they went. There were shrieks when a player failed to make a catch. One apple, hitting the ground, rolled towards where the Prince was hidden. It came to rest almost at his feet. Picking it up he stepped from behind the bush and walked towards the maidens. A hush fell on the garden and the games ceased when the startled girls saw the stranger coming towards them. They crowded together behind the girl in the embroidered dress. Ivan went up to her and, bowing low, held out the apple. She hesitated for a while, as if afraid, and then she quickly took it.

'Thank you,' she said, 'but—you startled us, sir, suddenly appearing from nowhere.'

'Not from nowhere,' Ivan replied, 'but from behind that bush. Last night, when walking in the forest, I saw this wall and climbed over it. I spent the night here and hid when you approached. My name is Ivan. Pray tell me yours.'

'Oh, I am the Princess', she answered, 'but there is no time for us to talk. You must leave this garden at once, for you are in great danger.'

'Danger?' asked the Prince. 'Surely you girls will not attack me!'

'No, no,' said the Princess, 'but you are in the garden of the wizard Koschtchei*.'

'Koschtchei,' Ivan echoed, 'I have never heard of him, but I am prepared to do battle with him.'

'You cannot fight him with ordinary weapons,' said the Princess anxiously. 'He will cast a spell and make you his slave.'

'Or turn you to stone,' another girl added.

'Or torture you,' said another.

'Escape before it is too late,' pleaded the Princess, 'for we ourselves cannot escape: we are all under his spell and must remain here in his castle for ever. Only for one hour each day are we allowed out into this garden.'

'I will not go and leave you to this evil monster,' the Prince retorted, 'I have never yet run away from danger and will not do so now.'

Just then a great gong boomed out and the frightened girls fled quickly through the archway. Surprised by this sudden move, the Prince stood for a few moments and watched the retreating figures. Then he raced after them, but he was too late. The great gates closed in his face, and once again he was alone in the garden.

* Pronounced Kush-chay.

CHAPTER IV

IN KOSCHTCHEI'S POWER

K NOWING that he could not force open the gates Ivan
started to climb the high wall, for he was determined
to rescue the Princess and her friends from the wizard's
power. His progress was slow and difficult, for the garden side
of the wall was very smooth and footholds were few. So occu-
pied was he with his task, and so quiet was the garden, that a
sudden loud noise startled him and he almost fell to the ground.
The gates burst open and masses of weird figures poured in,
running, leaping, stumbling, and crawling. Once these had
been ordinary men, but now they were Koschtchei's creatures,
transformed by his spells into misshapen monsters. Some had
huge heads with eyes as big as saucers and teeth like tigers'.
Others had long arms which almost touched the ground as they
ambled along like apes. A few, with outstretched hands, tried
to feel their way forward for they were blind. All of them ran
hither and thither, this way and that, like a pack of hounds
seeking their prey.

At last they saw the Prince clinging to the wall and, scream-
ing and screeching, they ran towards him. Long arms reached
upwards and pulled him to the ground. Strong arms seized him
and dragged him to the middle of the lawn. Then a sudden
hush fell over the garden. The monsters drew back, leaving

Suddenly the gate burst open

Ivan standing alone, as other figures were seen approaching through the gateway. First came Koschtchei's bodyguard of twenty warriors with great glistening bodies and leopard-skin cloaks. Behind them was the evil wizard himself, a terrifying figure. Cruel eyes stared from his deathly white face, with its hook nose and pointed beard. His long thin legs and arms, his hunched back over which there was a black cloak, gave him the appearance of a huge beetle. Silently he approached the Prince and fixed his evil eyes on him. Slowly he raised his arms before him with his outstretched fingers pointing towards Ivan. He was about to put the Prince under a spell.

Suddenly his magic-making was interrupted. The beautiful Princess and her twelve companions ran into the garden and up to where the wizard stood. On bended knees and with tears in their eyes they implored Koschtchei to spare the Prince. He snarled at them and bade his guards take them away. Turning towards Ivan he raised his hands again and muttered strange words. The Prince sank to the ground as he felt the strength leaving his body. He was powerless to defend himself. He wondered what evil Koschtchei was planning. Was he to be killed, or tortured, or changed into a horrible monster? For a second time the wizard raised his hands. Ivan

The evil wizard

* 49 *

could see Koschtchei's lips moving as he spoke, but he could no longer hear him. He felt a strange numbness in his limbs. The wizard's hands rose for a third time. It was then that Ivan remembered the feather that the Firebird had given him. Summoning his remaining strength he pulled it from his pocket and waved it weakly in the air.

CHAPTER V

THE MAGIC EGG

A T once Ivan's signal for help was answered. The Firebird suddenly appeared in a blaze of light. Swooping
down from the sky, it dived swiftly towards Koschtchei. Its fiery feathers brushed against him as it passed, and
the wizard staggered back bewildered. Down the bird came

The Firebird to the rescue

again, but this time it flew low over the heads of the wizard's monsters and his bodyguard, and their eyes were dazzled by its brilliance. It continued its low circling: there was magic in its movements. All who watched it were drawn towards it. They were attracted by its flaming colours as moths are to a light. They followed it as the children followed the Pied Piper. Across the grass and round the apple trees it glided with the monsters never far behind. At first they were trotting slowly after it, but soon the Firebird began to fly more quickly and the trotting changed to running. Faster still the Firebird flew, between the bushes, round the trees, across the lawn and back again, and still the evil monsters rushed after it. Even Koschtchei, whose magic was not as strong as the Firebird's, had been compelled to join the chase. Again the bird increased its speed, but it was too much for the pursuers. Panting and puffing, gasping and groaning, they sank down on the ground exhausted. The Firebird then flew over them with a slow swaying movement and soon the wizard and all his company were asleep.

'Now is your chance,' said the Firebird, alighting near the Prince. 'While Koschtchei and all his creatures sleep, go to his castle and seize the egg.'

'The egg?' asked the puzzled Prince.

'In Koschtchei's den,' said the bird, 'is a golden casket. In the casket is a large white egg as large as a man's head. Break the egg and Koschtchei with all his evil will disappear. Go quickly now!'

Jumping over the sleeping bodies, Ivan ran out through the archway, and up the stone stairway into the deserted castle. He went quickly from room to room, his footsteps echoing through the empty building. At last he found the wizard's den with its books and bottles, its snake skins and skulls. In a large cupboard he found what he was seeking. Carrying the shining casket in both hands he made his way back to the garden. The

Koschtchei pleaded for his life

sleeping figures were beginning to move, tossing and turning as they awakened. Going quickly to the centre of the lawn, where not long before he had suffered from Koschtchei's magic, Ivan put the casket on the ground and raised the lid. By this time everybody had woken up. They heard Koschtchei's cry of terror as the Prince lifted the giant egg and held it up for all to see. He tossed it high in the air, and the wizard screamed again, but Ivan caught it safely as it fell. Koschtchei, with every limb trembling, staggered up to the Prince and fell grovelling at his feet. While he pleaded for his life Ivan taunted him by tossing the egg lightly from one hand to the other. Finally, tired of teasing, Ivan dashed the egg to the ground. There was a deafening noise as it shattered into thousands of pieces and everything went dark for a while.

When the light returned Koschtchei and his castle had disappeared. No trace was left of the wizard and his evil. Monsters had become men again and the blind could see. How excited they all were when they realized the spell had been broken! Some sang and danced, others cried with joy. The Princess, followed by her friends, made her way through the happy crowd until she found the Prince.

'We wish to thank you,' she said as she curtsied low before him, 'for our freedom.'

'Do not thank me,' replied Ivan, 'you must thank the Firebird'—but it had disappeared too.

After the wedding

CHAPTER VI

PRINCE IVAN MARRIES

THE hot summer had ended and autumn had come, bringing with it some gentle rain. The earth was no longer parched and the faded fields were green again. Brown, russet, and yellow leaves decorated the trees and the village was decorated too. Flags and streamers hung from every window. Villagers in their best clothes thronged the streets. People had come from miles around to see the wedding of Prince Ivan and the Princess. They all rushed forward when the Prince arrived at the church in a golden carriage drawn by four white horses. They bowed and curtsied as the King and Queen drew near. They rushed forward again when the Princess appeared with her twelve maidens. The great church was crowded and hundreds who could not get in stood outside in groups, waiting until the service ended. At last the bells rang out from the tower and heralds played a fanfare on their trumpets. There was a great cheer when the bride and bridegroom came down the steps arm in arm. All eyes were on the happy pair, or nearly all eyes. Some who looked up said that they saw a large bird circling over the village, a bird with bright yellow and red feathers which glowed like a fire, a bird whose eyes flashed like diamonds, a bird with wings like flames.

CHAPTER VII

THE MUSIC

ABOUT how many words do you think there are in the
Firebird story that you have just read? Make a guess before looking for the answer at the bottom of this page.*
I think that you will agree this is a large number, yet strangely
enough, this story is often told without using any words at all.
This is done by turning it into a ballet. In ballet there is no
speaking as there is in a play—the story is told by miming and
dancing. There are costumes and scenery and, because of the
dancing, orchestral music is always an important part of ballet.

The music of *Firebird* was composed by Igor Stravinsky, who
was born near the Russian city of St. Petersburg, now called
Leningrad, in 1882. This ballet was first performed in Paris in
1910 and was a great success. Its French title is *L'Oiseau de Feu*
(oiseau = bird, feu = fire). Later, Stravinsky arranged a suite
from the ballet, known as the 'Firebird' suite, which is often
performed at concerts. Try to see this ballet if you can. If not,
perhaps you will be able to get a recording of the 'Firebird'
suite for your record-player. You will need to play it more than
once—in fact, many times, before you will really get to know
it. There are not many tunes in this suite that you can success-
fully play on the piano, violin, or recorder, but here are three
for you to try.

* About 3,200.

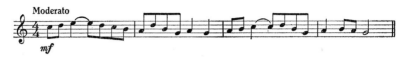

The tune above, and the one below are heard when Ivan meets the Princesses in the garden (Chapter III).

The tune above is taken from a Russian folk-song.

The next tune is heard when the story reaches its happy ending and Koschtchei and his castle have disappeared (Chapter V). This tune also is from a Russian folk-song.